CW00863798

Written by J Ayoola

How we love our hair

*Learning the basics about
caring for your hair*

Designed by Pelumi I

An Epoch Publishing Ltd

Text Copyright © 2019 by J Ayoola
Illustration Copyright © 2019 by Pelumi Igunnubole & J Ayoola
All rights reserved. No part of this book may be used or reproduced in any manner without the written permission except in the case of brief quotations embodied in critical articles or reviews.

Book design by Pelumi Igunnubole at www.pelumii.com
For more information contact:
www.howweloveourhair.com
Instagram at howweloveourhairbooks
ISBN: 978-1-9163364-0-7
Printed in the United Kingdom

First Published April 2020

"I praise you because you made me
in an amazing and wonderful way.
What you have done is wonderful.
I know this very well."

- King David the Psalmist -

I would like to thank Ebony Ngwa for her inspiration and Val, Berry and Nisha for their encouragement and support.

To Faith Adomah, Adanne Lee, Dara Lloyds, Alarni Sylvester-Williams, Somiji Grace Igunnubole and Sarah Adeyemi, thank you all for inspiring this book.

Chapter 01

Why I love my hair

My name is Amelia, and I love my hair. Let me tell you about some of the things it can do.

Twists that spring
back and forth when
I play with it.

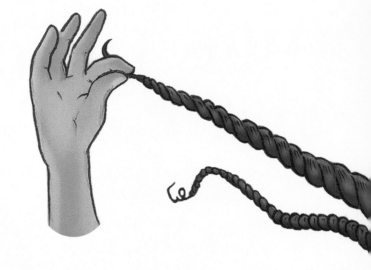

Curls that bounce,
s t r e t c h
and pop back into place.

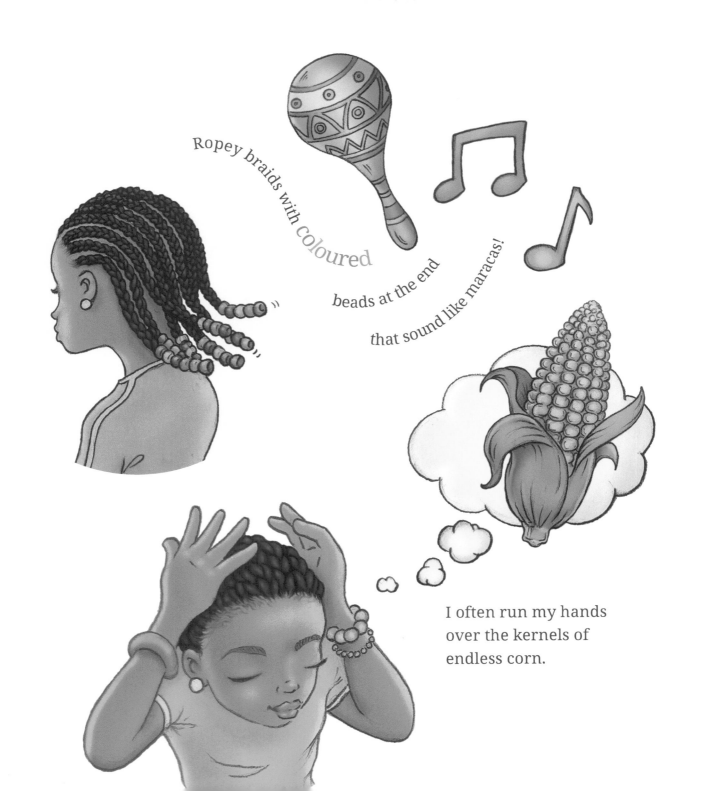

Ropey braids with coloured beads at the end that sound like maracas!

I often run my hands over the kernels of endless corn.

Or, **squeeze** my fat twists that feel like twisted marshmallows.

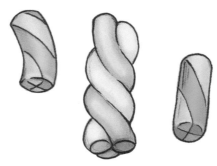

There are so many different styles
to choose from but my favourite
style of all....

...is the lion's mane...

ROARRR

Now let's go and meet some of my friends.
We all have *curly hair* with different textures
and curl shapes that create beautiful patterns.

Some **big** and small, and some tiny mixed
with even tinier curls. All shapes and sizes come
together to create the amazing pattern of curls
in our hair.

Chapter 02

What I use to love my hair

I am Ebony Rose, and like my friend Amelia, I want to share a secret about our hair.

My favourite hobby on a summer's day is to water the flowers and plants in our garden. We have daisies, tulips and sunflowers to name a few and time flies by when I am in the garden with my watering can taking care of my plants.

Our colourful garden reminds me of my hair. Imagine you
have a baby plant that you want to grow and one day you
realise it's been a very long time since you last watered it.
In fact, so long that the stalk and apple green leaves have
gone all wrinkly and limp.

Well, I have learned that our
hair works the same way.

If we don't water our hair,
it gets thirsty too, so my big
sister Violet makes sure that
every day we remember to
drink the right amount.

When I drink plenty of water my hair drinks it too, straight from the roots - it's just like watering the soil around my sunflowers. I even water my hair on the outside, but I don't use a watering can. Instead, I use my super spritz bottle, which is filled with a secret potion to make my liquorice looking strands soft.

I shake, shake, shake my bottle,

then evenly spritz water all over my hair. I can always tell when I have used the right amount of water because my hair feels soft but not too damp.

Inside my spray bottle contains

"The magic 3!"

- rosewater,
- vegetable glycerin
- and water.

Rosewater is made from the petals of a rose, it is my favourite scent and is one of my mother's secret beauty ingredients. In some cultures it is used for perfume as part of a ceremony, in the country India it is used to make delicious sweets, but in our home, we use it to keep our hair healthy.

The next magical ingredient is glycerin.

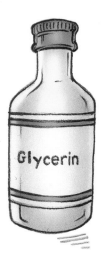

It's extra special because it attracts teeny weeny water droplets from the air to my hair. These water droplets are so tiny I cannot see them, it draws water droplets to my hair like a bee attracted to pollen in a flower. Once it is there, it nourishes it by making sure my hair is not thirsty, really is quite magical.

The final part is adding water which Mother uses the purest and cleanest of them all.

It all goes into my spritz bottle then I shake it hard to make sure all the magic is mixed in together. I then lightly spray it all over my hair and sometimes I get tiny droplets on my face but that's okay. I love the smell of rosewater.

Sometimes I feel like using

another secret recipe
which contains
- water,
- coconut oil
- and aloe vera juice.

My favourite oil to use is coconut oil. It smells so delicious, plus coconut is one of my favourite fruits to eat.

And you are probably wondering
what aloe vera juice is, well it is the
juice that comes from the aloe vera
plant, we have this plant in our garden.
Sometimes when I am playing in it,
I get bitten by an insect.

When that happens, my mother will
clean the bite and cut a piece of our
aloe vera plant to soothe it, which
makes it better. It has some amazing
qualities and is also great for hair
helping it to stay soft and healthy.
You have likely walked past it before
in your local grocery shop or market.

So there you go, I have let you into a little secret on what my family and I use to keep our hair nourished and moisturised so it can grow healthy.

Chapter 03

When I love my hair

Hey, welcome, I'm Lola, and like Ebony Rose, I make sure my hair always stays soft.

In my spare time, I read
detective books on finding
clues and how to catch
a criminal.

Now, water has become a good
friend in keeping my hair super soft.
However, it's also very cheeky because
it's always trying to escape, leaving
my hair feeling dry again. I call it the
great escaper!

Since the water is always planning its e s c a p e '
I have become a detective and worked out just how to stop it.

Shhh, it's top secret, so I will have to whisper, but this is how I do it.

After spraying my hair with water like Ebony Rose, I use hair cream and follow up with a hair butter or oil to trap the cheeky water inside.

I *gently* part my hair in sections with my fingers.

I take a small amount of cream and rub it between my hands, watching it become soft and shiny. Then, I massage it through small sections of my hair.

I then repeat this step with my hair butter or oil.

Doing this leaves my hair
feeling super fluffy and
keeps that cheeky water from
escaping, well at least for
a while until it starts feeling
dry and I repeat it all
over again.

I do this every few days
depending on how my hair
feels, but my friend Keke
says she does it once a week.
She also only uses a liquid
spritz and hair cream because
a heavy butter or oil makes
her hair too greasy. I guess
everyone's hair need is
a little different.

Looking after my hair is detective work. I am always keeping an eye on it, looking for clues to make sure it stays healthy.

Chapter 04

How I Love My Hair

My name is Keke, and like Lola, I love my hair too. I enjoy skiing in winter down the slopes and discovering new places to ski is one of my favourite things to do.

I am learning that knowing how to comb and finger detangle my hair keeps it healthy and free to grow. My hair is full of many types of curls; spirals that look just like the metal coil inside a pen.

And, in some places, loops that resemble a rainbow magic spring. Because my hair is mixed with coils and curls, the hair strands often get caught on each other, becoming tangled together like best friends hugging.

So I have to keep my hair tangle free, and I do this very carefully. First I check to see whether it is dry. If it feels crunchy, crispy or dry, I moisturise my hair with hair spritz and my hair oil or butter just like Lola.

But, if it feels soft, I put my hair in large sections, twisting or braiding each one as I go along.

I leave the last part loose as this will be the first one I comb.

I take a small amount of the loose hair. Then I clamp it between my thumb and first two fingers and glide a bit like skiing down a slope.

As I ski through my hair, I am gently taking out any tangles along the way. I start towards the bottom of my hair working my way upwards.

Once all of the knots and tangles are out, I use a wide-tooth comb, gently gliding it from the bottom of my hair to the roots. This step takes out any remaining knots and tangles I might have missed.

If I feel a tangle, I stop.

Then, using my thumb and fingers, I gently untangle it. I do this throughout my whole head until I finish. What makes it even more enjoyable is I usually do this while watching my favourite movie.

Chapter 05

How I love my hair in seasons

Hi there, I am Mercy, and I am learning about the different ways to love my hair in each season.

I have always been interested in how one season changes into another. My favourite season is spring, and every year I look forward to seeing the buds beginning to form on the blossom tree outside our house.

Each day I wake up and rush to my bedroom window to see whether I can tell if the buds on the tree have bloomed a little more. I have always been fascinated by it and became even more intrigued when I discovered that our hair works in a similar way.

Our hair has seasons similar
to spring, summer, autumn
and winter.

Sometimes when combing or braiding my hair
I notice that hair falls out in the comb. So, to make
sure it's not damaged hair I study it carefully. I can
always tell that it is old hair because at the top of
the strand I see a little white bulb.

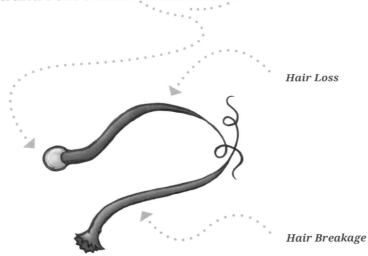

Hair Loss

Hair Breakage

This bulb lets me know that it is not broken but has
finished its cycle. So when it falls out, as long as it
has the little white tip, I know that it is autumn for
that piece of hair*. If it doesn't have a white bulb
I know, it's broken, and maybe I need to be gentler
or moisturise my hair more.

*White bulb can also be an indication that you are pulling your hair too tight causing premature hair loss

You are probably wondering what happens once
it falls out. Well, it's just like the seasons. In autumn
the leaves begin to fall off the trees, and in winter
the trees are bare and silent. So for a little while,
it's winter when our scalp is resting. Then when
it's ready, it's spring again.

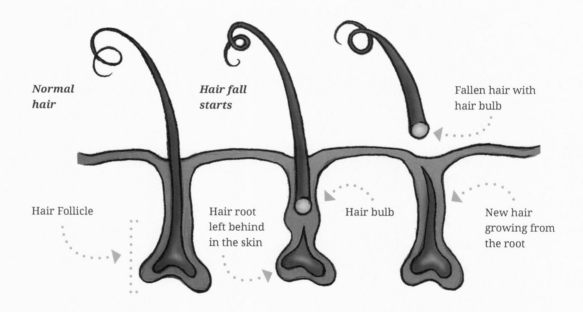

*Normal
hair*

*Hair fall
starts*

Fallen hair with
hair bulb

Hair Follicle

Hair root
left behind
in the skin

Hair bulb

New hair
growing from
the root

In spring, in the area where the piece
of hair fell out, new hair begins to
bud from the roots like trees budding
in nature.

In summer, the buds on the trees become
full-blown leaves, or flowers, depending on the
tree, just like your hair as it begins to flourish
and grow. On average, the summer phase can
last between three to seven years depending
on your hair, for some people it can last a little
longer. The amazing thing is that all the seasons
happen at different times for each strand,
so you are never without any hair.

Chapter 06

How I love my hair at bedtime

My name is Jasmine, and
I am getting ready for bed.
I sleep in fresh cotton sheets
and rest my head on a big
fluffy pillow, wrapped in
a cotton pillowcase.

My bed is very cosy, and with my cuddly toys to keep me company sleeping is all the more enjoyable.

As lovely as my cotton sheets are to sleep in, they are not the best material for my hair. You see, our hair is very delicate due to its kinks and curls, and when we toss and turn while we sleep, the cotton rubs on our hair, causing dryness and breakage. So, to be safe, I tuck my hair up for bed by using a satin or silk bonnet, or scarf, I make sure that it is secure, but not too tight.

When I wake up in the morning and remove it from my head, my hair is tidy and soft, but sometimes I forget to braid and wrap my hair at night, and in the morning I look like this...

My little brother says
I could scare a monster.

So guess what? If ever I am afraid of the dark before I go to bed, I leave my bonnet off. That way, instead of the bedtime monster scaring me, I scare it away with my amazing lion's mane... roarrrr!

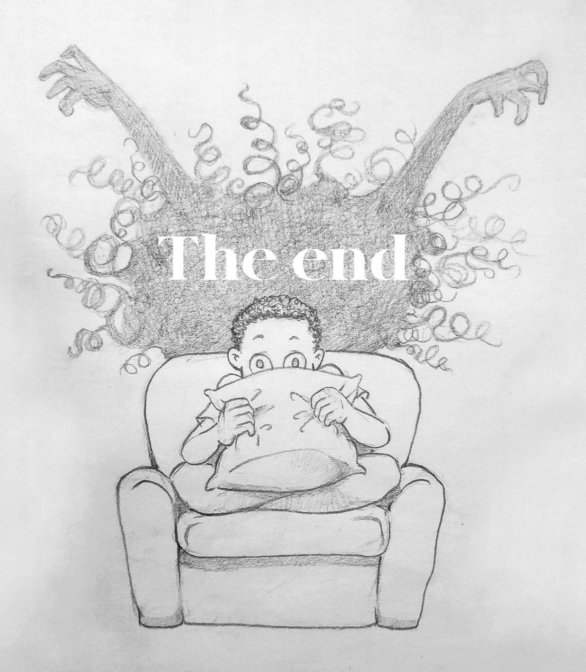

Quiz time!

Now let's see how much you have learned...

1. What is Amelia's favourite hairstyle?

- ☐ Marshmallows
- ☐ Strawberry curls
- ☐ The lion's mane

2. Ebony Rose uses _____ on both the inside and outside to keep her hair healthy.

- ☐ Water
- ☐ Oil
- ☐ Plants

3. What did Keke say her hair feels like when she should not comb it?

- ☐ Soft
- ☐ Dry
- ☐ Wet

4. Jasmine tucks her hair up at bedtime to stop it from _____, keeping it soft and tidy.

- ☐ Becoming loose
- ☐ Breaking
- ☐ Growing

5. What does Lola use to stop the great escape?

- ☐ Hair butter and oil
- ☐ Aloe vera
- ☐ Magnifying glass

6. When Keke skis through her hair with her fingers or wide tooth comb, she removes _____ & _____.

- ☐ Ice & water
- ☐ Oil & butter
- ☐ Knots & tangles

7. What do both Ebony Rose and Lola use if their hair feels dry?

- ☐ Comb
- ☐ Brush
- ☐ Water

8. Why do you need to stop that cheeky water escaping?

- ☐ To prevent dryness
- ☐ To keep your hair wet

9. What does Mercy look for when a strand of hair falls out?

- ☐ White bulb
- ☐ Seasons
- ☐ Softness

10. What does Ebony Rose do with her spritz bottle before she sprays her hair?

- ☐ Uses a magic wand
- ☐ Shakes it
- ☐ Drinks it

Answers

1-3 out of 10

Good try. Read through the sections again to make sure you understand it.

4-5 out of 10

You are getting there. Now that you have seen the questions read through the chapters again to make sure you understand everything.

6-7 out of 10

Well done. Remember, by putting what you have learned in to practice you will get better and better with time.

8-9 out of 10

Great. You know how to keep your hair looking and feeling healthy.

10 out of 10

Fantastic. You are a super hair lover. Remember, everyone's hair is unique to them. Over time, you can add to what you have already learned, and your hair will continue to thrive.

Lightning Source UK Ltd.
Milton Keynes UK
UKHW050536091020
371274UK00002BA/42